D1398363

MY  EASTER EGG HUNT

MY EASTER EGG HUNT

Rosie Smith & Bruce Whatley

SCHOLASTIC INC.

For Ana, Mark and little Rafael — RS and BW

Hunting for eggs is fun.

Look up.

Look down.

Look under.

Look around.

Look over.

Look through.

Look inside . . .

and outside too.

Hunting for eggs is fun

when you share with everyone.

First published by Scholastic Australia in 2013

No part of this publication may be reproduced, stored in a retrieval system, or transmitted in any form or by any means, electronic, mechanical, photocopying, recording, or otherwise, without written permission of the publisher. For information regarding permission, write to Scholastic Press, an imprint of Scholastic Australia Pty Limited, PO Box 579, Gosford, NSW 2250, Australia.

ISBN 978-0-545-64306-1

Text and illustrations copyright © 2013 by Introspective Bear. All rights reserved. Published by Scholastic Inc., 557 Broadway, New York, NY 10012, by arrangement with Scholastic Press, an imprint of Scholastic Australia Pty Limited. SCHOLASTIC and associated logos are trademarks and/or registered trademarks of Scholastic Inc.

12 11 10 9 8 7 6 5 4 3 2   14 15 16 17 18 19/0

Printed in the U.S.A.   40

This edition first printing, March 2014

Typeset in Goudy Children